Rehabilitating Mr. Wiggles

Vol. 1

by Neil Swaab

Rehabilitating Mr. Wiggles was previously published twice a week in:

The Daily Orange Newspaper (August 1999 – May 2000)

and is currently published weekly in:

Real Detroit Weekly (June 2000 – current)

NY Press (August 2000 – current)

and monthly in:

Gear Magazine (June 2001 – current)

New comics are posted weekly at www.neilswaab.com

Write to Neil Swaab at mail@neilswaab.com

1 2 3 4 5 6 7 8 9 10

ISBN 0-9722182-0-3 First Printing

For the fans.

–N.S.

INTRODUCTION

If you aren't already familiar with the comic strip, *Rehabilitating Mr. Wiggles*, then, please, don't buy this book. Don't look through it or stop and read a few of the comics contained herein. Just put it down and walk away. Go home to your living room, microwave a bag of popcorn, settle in to watch an episode of Everybody Loves Raymond, and fall asleep, drooling into your pillow. Forget you'd ever stumbled upon this book. Because, in all honesty, nothing good can come from reading it.

Rehabilitating Mr. Wiggles won't enlighten you or help you get more joy out of life. It won't make you cool, or popular, or more attractive to the opposite sex. It won't cure baldness or increase breast size. It isn't a substitute for whatever's missing in your existence. This book is not the answer to your job woes, your spiritual woes or your love woes. It's just a collection of comic strips, and reading them will not make you a better person. In fact, quite the opposite.

If you read this book you'll turn bitter and resentful. You'll laugh at other people's misfortunes. You'll push elderly women down crowded flights of stairs and set fire to small animals. You'll consider selling crack to children and then children to cults. You'll smack your lips at the idea of riding naked, obese men to work in the morning and turn giddy at the thought of self-gratification through time-travel. You might even fall down to your knees, crying on the bathroom floor, hugging your toilet screaming "There is no God! There is no God!" over and over again.

But worst of all, you might laugh. A lot. At horribly disgusting and inappropriate things. Things that should never have been put down on paper, let alone published and distributed. And then you'll have to sit down and wonder why you laughed. You'll have to analyze yourself and possibly look at the world in a different way. This book could change your life and you don't want that. Because change is scary.

So best to just put it down now and walk away towards that whiny, droning noise in the back of your head. It's Ray Romano calling you. He wants you to love him. Are you going to answer?

A NOTE ABOUT THE COMPILATION

This book contains the first 140 Rehabilitating Mr. Wiggles comic strips to be published, representing close to three years of work. I believe that everything one does should be a learning experience, and this comic is no exception. You'll notice that the style changes radically from beginning to end as I grew as both an artist and a writer over that time period. I ask that you not judge the art on the early comics too harshly, but view them as I do– as the beginnings to something great and unique. Also, I'd like to note that a few of the comics reference the events of Sept. 11, 2001, during which time I was, and still am, living in New York. I point this out because, out of context, the comic with the American flag (p. 51) seems somewhat out of place in the compilation but, being a weekly comic, it reflects what was going on at the time and, thusly was included. Finally, I'd like to also note that the last comic with Jesus (p. 71) is the uncensored version, different than what was originally published. I obviously did not want to make the changes and present it here as it originally should have been viewed. Enjoy.

Rehabilitating Mr. Wiggles

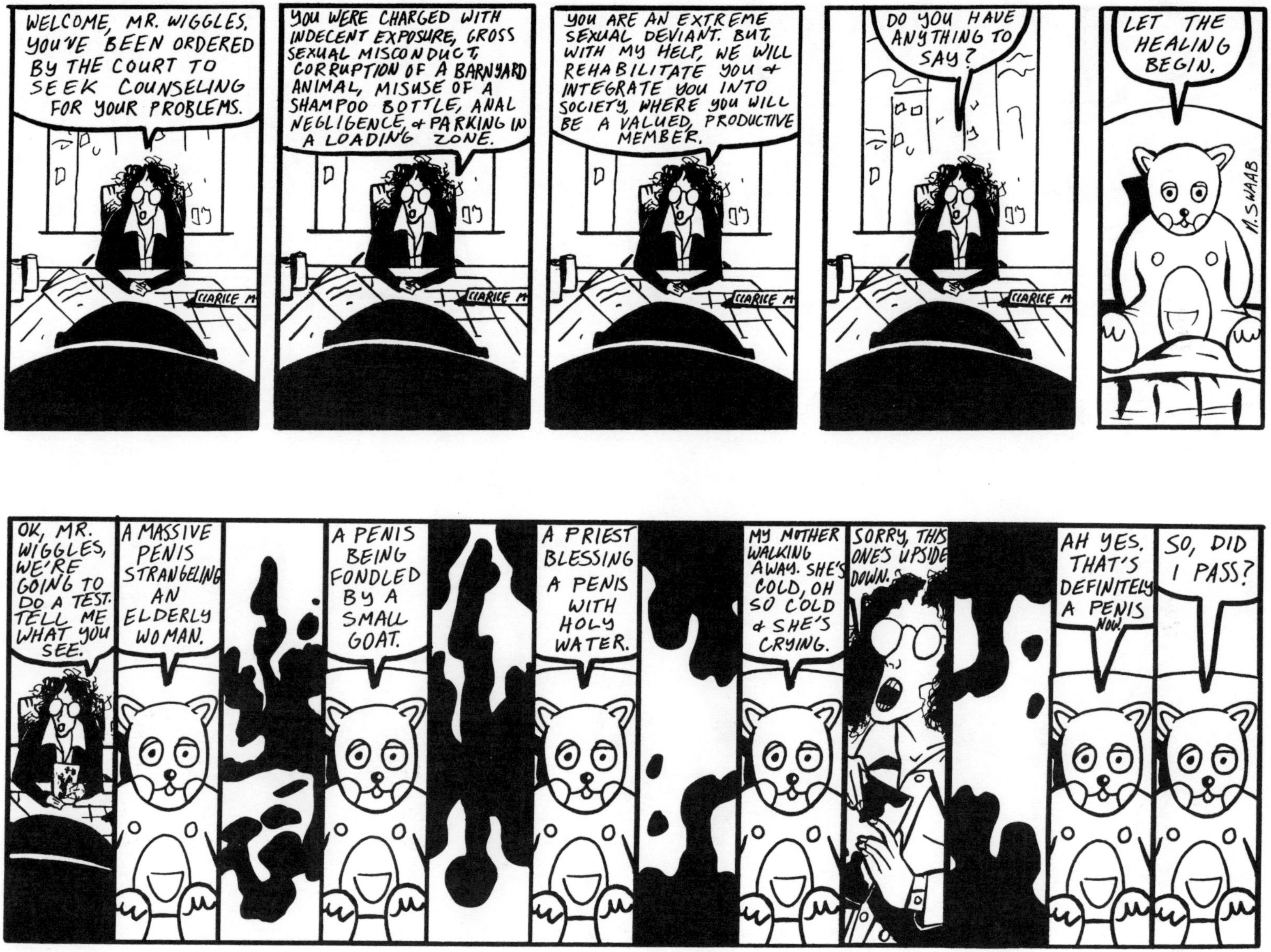

WELCOME, MR. WIGGLES. YOU'VE BEEN ORDERED BY THE COURT TO SEEK COUNSELING FOR YOUR PROBLEMS.
CLARICE M
YOU WERE CHARGED WITH INDECENT EXPOSURE, GROSS SEXUAL MISCONDUCT, CORRUPTION OF A BARNYARD ANIMAL, MISUSE OF A SHAMPOO BOTTLE, ANAL NEGLIGENCE, & PARKING IN A LOADING ZONE.
YOU ARE AN EXTREME SEXUAL DEVIANT. BUT, WITH MY HELP, WE WILL REHABILITATE YOU & INTEGRATE YOU INTO SOCIETY, WHERE YOU WILL BE A VALUED, PRODUCTIVE MEMBER.
DO YOU HAVE ANYTHING TO SAY?
LET THE HEALING BEGIN.
M.SWAAB
OK, MR. WIGGLES, WE'RE GOING TO DO A TEST. TELL ME WHAT YOU SEE.
A MASSIVE PENIS STRANGELING AN ELDERLY WOMAN.
A PENIS BEING FONDLED BY A SMALL GOAT.
A PRIEST BLESSING A PENIS WITH HOLY WATER.
MY MOTHER WALKING AWAY. SHE'S COLD, OH SO COLD & SHE'S CRYING.
SORRY, THIS ONE'S UPSIDE DOWN.
AH YES. THAT'S DEFINITELY A PENIS NOW.
SO, DID I PASS?

HEY, I'M COOKING DINNER. WOULD YOU LIKE A TEXAS HAMBURGER?
ISN'T THAT WHERE YOU EAT LUNCH-MEAT OUT OF YOUR NEIGHBOR'S ASSHOLE?
UH, I DON'T THINK SO.
THEN MAKE MINE A DOUBLE!
N. SWAAB

IS IT ME OR AM I THE ONLY ONE WHO FEELS THIS INSATIABLE NEED TO SPLATTER MY BRAINS ALL OVER THE WALL EVERY TIME I SEE AN OLD NAVY COMMERCIAL?
N. SWAAB
I'M SORRY, DID YOU SAY SOMETHING?
HEY, I DIDN'T KNOW MAGIC COULD HANG-GLIDE!

Rehabilitating Mr. Wiggles

I HAVE SO MUCH WORK TO DO. HOW AM I SUPPOSED TO FINISH IT ALL?
WHAT WORK? YOU DON'T **DO** ANYTHING.
I WISH I WAS IN JAIL. I COULD REALLY USE THE FREE TIME. IT WOULD BE GREAT! I'D GET SO MUCH DONE!
BUT WHAT ABOUT THE DAILY ANAL RAPINGS?
M. SWAAB
HEY, IT'S ONLY RAPE IF YOU DON'T WANT IT!
YOU ARE ONE SICK TEDDY.
EXCUSE ME, MISS? WE'RE TRYING TO RAISE MONEY TO FUND A PROJECT PROVIDING PORNOGRAPHY TO UNDERAGE CHILDREN OF BROKEN HOMES.
HELP THE CHILDREN
YOU SICKO!
GEEZ. THAT'S THE FOURTH PERSON WHO'S HIT ME THIS HOUR! WHY ARE PEOPLE SO AGAINST HELPING THE CHILDREN?
I DON'T KNOW. MAYBE IT WOULD WORK BETTER IF WE WERE WEARING PANTS.
YOU THINK?
COULDN'T HURT.
M. SWAAB

Neil Swaab

I HAD THE WEIRDEST DREAM LAST NIGHT, MR. WIGGLES. I DREAMT YOU CRAWLED INTO BED WITH ME & REPEATEDLY SODOMIZED ME WHILE I SLEPT, OVER & OVER & OVER AGAIN.
WHY ARE YOU SMILING?
N. SWAAB

YOU KNOW WHAT THE BEST THING ABOUT BEING A CHRISTIAN ROCKER IS?
JESUS PLAYED BASS
YOU'RE NEVER AT A LOSS FOR WHAT TO WRITE ABOUT.
OH, AND THE BLOW. LET'S NOT FORGET THE FREE BLOW.
N. SWAAB

THIS SUCKS. I'M SICK AGAIN. MY HEAD HURTS, I'M DRIPPING SNOT, I'M COUGHING, I'M LOSING MY VOICE.
I KEEP GETTING SICKER + SICKER. BY THE END OF THE WEEK I'LL PROBABLY BE DEAD.
NOT THAT YOU CARE.
SO, IF YOU DIE, CAN I HAVE YOUR ROOM?
JUST PEEL ME OFF THE BED.
M. SWAAB

HOW AM I SUPPOSED TO DO A COMIC TODAY? I FEEL LIKE SHIT. I'M CONGESTED, MY THROAT HURTS, I'M OOZING SNOT EVERYWHERE. IT FEELS LIKE A FAT, FRENCH PROSTITUTE'S SITTING ON MY FACE.
WELL, IT'S LIKE I SAY: WHATEVER DOESN'T KILL YOU ONLY MAKES YOU WEAKER & MORE CRIPPLED UNTIL DEATH FINALLY TAKES HOLD & YOU END UP DROWNING IN A POOL OF YOUR OWN FILTH.
WELL, IT'S SOMETHING TO LOOK FORWARD TO, ANYWAY.
M. SWAAB

I HAVE A COMIC IN THE D.O.
SUPER STAR
HA! HA! HA! HA! HA! HA!
PICK-UP LINES THAT REALLY REALLY REALLY DON'T WORK. #4
N. SWAAB

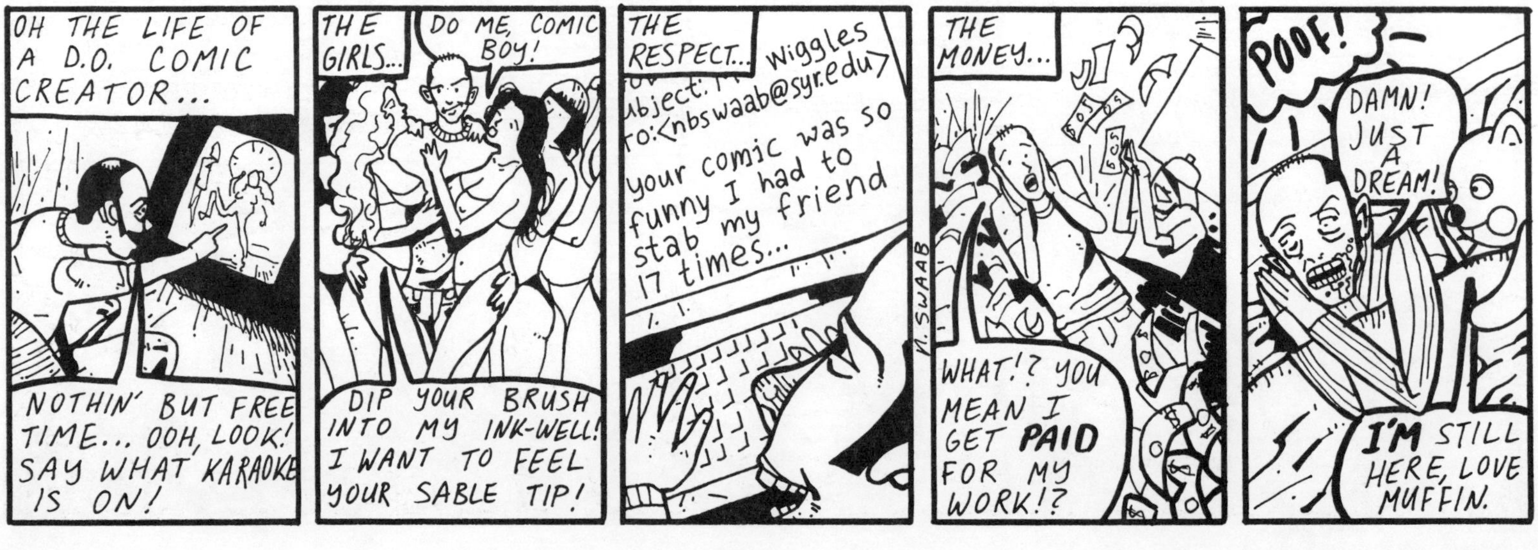
OH THE LIFE OF A D.O. COMIC CREATOR...
NOTHIN' BUT FREE TIME... OOH, LOOK! SAY WHAT KARAOKE IS ON!
THE GIRLS...
DO ME, COMIC BOY!
DIP YOUR BRUSH INTO MY INK-WELL! I WANT TO FEEL YOUR SABLE TIP!
THE RESPECT...
wiggles
ubject:
To:<nbswaab@syr.edu>
your comic was so funny I had to stab my friend 17 times...
N. SWAAB
THE MONEY...
WHAT!? YOU MEAN I GET PAID FOR MY WORK!?
POOF!
DAMN! JUST A DREAM!
I'M STILL HERE, LOVE MUFFIN.

Bookmarks Location: http://www.mutilation.com
DAVE'S GENITAL MUTILATION PAGE.COM!
censored
cutting
gore
the shocking
danger
bondage
Cock play/torture
testicular torture
castration play
fire/electro play
nailing
blood!blood!blood!
the hard stuff
start
www.mutilat...
THE INTERNET SCARES ME.
I LIKE IT WHEN THEY BLEED!
M.SWAAB
YOU'RE GOING AS THE UNI-BOMBER FOR HALLOWEEN, MR. WIGGLES?
IT'S HALLOWEEN?
NAUSEA
THE WIGGLES MANIFESTO
THE CATCHER IN THE RYE
PEOPLE TO KILL:
TNT
M.SWAAB

REHABILITATING MR. WIGGLES PRESENTS:
WHAT WERE YOU FOR HALLOWEEN?:
PEOPLE WHO OUTSMARTED THE SYSTEM BY NOT DRESSING UP. OR DID THEY?
I WENT AS ROCKER, MEATLOAF! ONLY... 180LB'S LIGHTER, & WITH BLOND HAIR, & AS A GIRL!
I WENT AS A GUY WITH NO PERCEPTION OF TIME! WHAT TIME IS IT!? DON'T ASK ME 'CAUSE I DON'T KNOW!
I WENT AS A SERIAL KILLER! I LOOK JUST LIKE EVERY ONE ELSE, BUT INSIDE I'M EVIL, OH SO EVIL!
I WENT AS A SEXUALLY PROMISCUOUS SORORITY GIRL! I GOT WASTED & FUCKED A DOZEN FRAT BOYS! I SPENT ALL MORNING WASHING SPLUGE OUT OF MY HAIR!
I WENT AS A GUY WHO STARES AT GIRLS BREASTS! BEST NIGHT OF MY LIFE!
I WENT AS MY FAVORITE SUPERHERO, DIRK SIDEBURNS! MESS WITH ME & I'LL SIDEBURN YOU TO DEATH!
I WENT AS A CRACK ADDICT, ONLY... I WASN'T PRETENDING. PLEASE, I NEED HELP!
I DIDN'T GO. NOBODY LIKES ME. PLEASE LOVE ME. PLEASE?
N. SWAAB

YOU'RE NOT THE LEAST BIT INTERESTED IN ME.
YOU'D RATHER EAT VOMIT INSTEAD OF MAKING OUT WITH ME.
NOTHING I DO COULD EVER PLEASE YOU. YOU'D LAUGH IF I DIED.
YOU'D SLEEP WITH MY FRIENDS & STEAL MY CAR.
N. SWAAB
YOU'RE JUST MY TYPE. WANNA DATE?

EXCITED ABOUT THE NEW SEASON OF E.R.?
THE COSTUME GIVE IT AWAY?
N. SWAAB

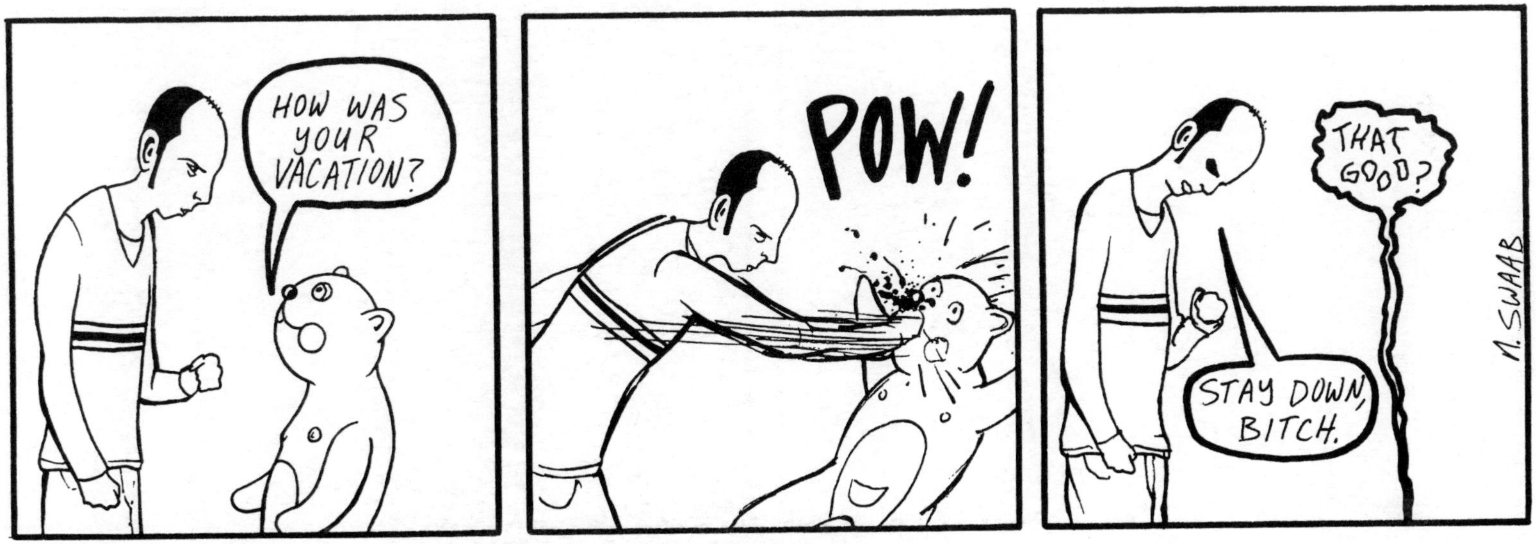
HOW WAS YOUR VACATION?
POW!
THAT GOOD?
STAY DOWN, BITCH.
N. SWAAB

THAT'S WHAT YOU SAID **LAST** TIME.
SHE **LOOKED** CLEAN!
PHARMAC
Scratch. Scratch.
N. SWAAB

I TALK A LOT ABOUT SICK, SEXUAL THINGS, BUT THOSE ARE JUST JOKES. I'M REALLY LIKE EVERYONE ELSE. I JUST WANT TO BE LOVED...
...BY 4 WOMEN AT ONCE, WHILE CHAINED TO A BED, & BEATEN WITH LEATHER RODS. I'M A BAD TEDDY! A BAD TEDDY! HURT ME!
LOVE ME?
N. SWAAB

Rehabilitating Mr. Wiggles

I CAN'T BELIEVE THE SEMESTER'S OVER. SO MANY DREAMS UNFULFILLED...
I NEVER WROTE THAT NOVEL ABOUT THE SQUIRREL EXHIBITIONIST, OR GOT THAT DRAGON TATTOOED ON MY BACK, OR FELL IN LOVE.
IN THE END I'M STILL, SADLY, ALONE.
YOU'VE GOT ME...
WANNA FUCK?
M.SWAAB
I FARTED IN YOUR FACE WHILE YOU SLEPT.
THAT'S OK. I DUG UP YOUR MOTHER'S CORPSE AND SODOMIZED IT ALL NIGHT LONG.
BUT MY MOTHER'S STILL ALIVE...
WHO THE HELL WAS THAT THEN?
M.SWAAB

I'VE HAD ANAL SEX WITH 50 GUYS.
I LET GUYS COME ON MY FACE, MY HAIR, MY BREASTS. I EAT THE STUFF UP.
I ONCE SUCKED OFF A DOG.
BUT I'D **NEVER** LET A GUY PUT HIS PENIS IN MY VAGINA. I'M NO SLUT. I WANT TO STAY **PURE** FOR MY FUTURE HUSBAND.
DON'T YOU JUST **LOVE** TECHNICAL VIRGINS?
N. SWAAB

i'm sick of never keeping my New Year's resolutions. so this year i made some i knew i could keep.
from now on i plan to be lazier, more self-centered, more judgemental, & unkinder towards my fellow man.
so how's that going?
i'll let you know when i start, shit-head.
N. SWAAB

Rehabilitating Mr. Wiggles

this comic is plagued with filth and grossness. as part of the new year i resolve to make it more sophisticated.
from now on, no more penis jokes.
are you sure?
absolutely! i can be funny on a whole variety of topics, like... um... hmm... uh... well... maybe...
damn, this is hard...
pun intended?
M. SWAAB

i hate dating. it's nerve-wracking, painful, & embarrassing. i get so nervous that i say & do all the wrong things & somehow manage to mess everything up.
why can't you just skip dating & go right into the safety & comfort of a loving relationship?
because that would be easy & stress-free, & what fun would **that** be?
damn you & your teddy-bear logic.
M. SWAAB

i started doing these penis exercises i found on the web.
©neil swaab 2000
they're supposed to enhance function by strengthening the muscles through an intense regimen of work-outs and con-ditioning.
so, how's that going?
well, my penis is swollen, bloody, and painful not only to touch, but also to look at.
so, it's working?
better than ever.
N. SWAAB

hello, sir. you've been chosen to testmarket my new brand of ice-cream marketed specifically for sex offenders in hopes that it will satis-fy your perverted urges, thus end-ing these crimes.
i call it "guilty pleasures."
mmm... tastes like young boys...
yes, that's our most popular flavor, "pre-teen passion". it also comes in "forcible sodomy," "anal delights," and "barn-yard sur-prise."
but this hasn't curbed my appetites, only in-creased them.
uh-oh.
say, you're kind of cute.
N. SWAAB

Rehabilitating Mr. Wiggles

you ever think of working out?
i should. my body's disgusting. it's thin, & boney, & i've got hair in all the wrong places.
it's scary. children run in fear at the sight of my naked body.
Why are you showing children your naked body?
it was a crime of passion. let it go.
M. SWAAB
what's all **this**, mr. wiggles?
this is my new cosmetic line for the homely. i call it, "hidden blessings."
Before
After
but it's just a paper bag with a drawn-on face.
exactly! let's face it, putting make-up on never really makes ugly girls more attractive only less repulsive.
After
this eliminates the problem **entirely**!
After
reminds me of a porno i once saw...
reminds me of a porno i once **did**!
M. SWAAB

can you believe that Valentine's Day is only a week away and i'm alone again as usual?
we need to find you a woman.
it's hopeless. the only women who like me are worse off than myself. i'm a magnet for the morbidly obese and shut-ins,
you know, people who can't leave their homes due to phy-sical disfig-urement.
and when i do meet a nice girl, they won't return any of my phone-calls.
well, they're the ones missing out.
really? because they don't seem to be missing anything. in fact they seem to be having quite a great time.
they're faking it.
what are you, Channeling the voice of my mother?
yes, now stand up straight & clean that pig-stye you call a room.
N. SWAAB

mr. wiggles, i met this girl the other night, & one thing led to another, & now i'm feeling things i've never felt before.
is it love?
i don't know. does love burn when you urinate?
only the good kind, my friend, only the good kind...
N. SWAAB

wanna go back to my place and do it teddy-bear style?
A.SWAAB

touch it! touch it!
A.SWAAB
pick-up lines to try at parties. #17.

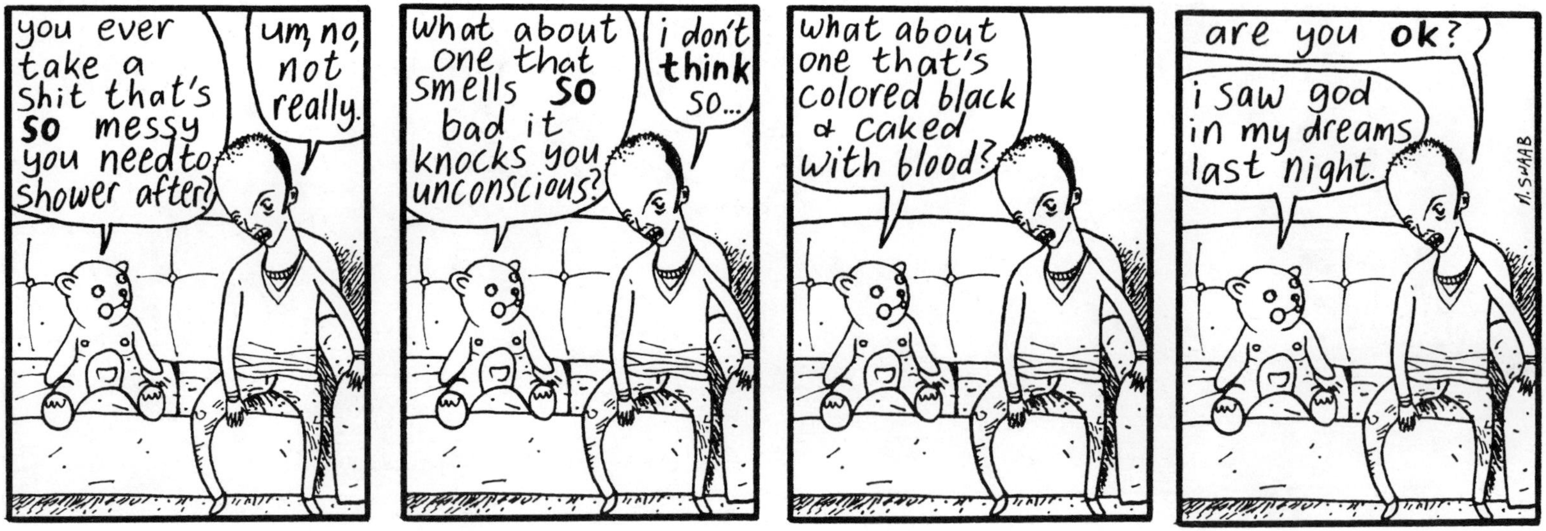
you ever take a shit that's **so** messy you need to shower after?
um, no, not really.
what about one that smells **so** bad it knocks you unconscious?
i don't **think** so...
what about one that's colored black & caked with blood?
are you **ok**?
i saw god in my dreams last night.
N. SWAAB

what are you doing there, mr. wiggles?
i've decided to become an artist. i've been painting for days. i call this piece, "Mother, the Earth is Round."
but all i see is a girl peeing.
exactly! it deals with the social implications of a monotheistic society. my previous piece was a tribute to Bertrand Russel entitled "Iron Dionysus."
but this is just **another** picture of a girl peeing. in fact, your whole **studio** is covered with paintings of girls peeing. what's the deal?
hey, Monet painted water lillies, i paint girls peeing. we're kindred spirits.
i don't know, did Monet paint with a full erection?
the man always painted sitting down. do i need to say more?

mr. wiggles, did you take a crap in the sink?
yes, it's part of a piece i'm working on. i've decided to become a performance artist.
crapping in other people's sinks & leaving it there for them to "discover" is not art.
hey, anything's art if you do it in a black sweater.
M. SWAAB

i love the Salvation Army! what could be better than buying people's old and discarded things for bargain prices?
HOMER'S THE ODYSSEY
TRUER THAN
SENIOR CITIZEN DAYS ON WEDNESDAYS
SPRING
look! wednesdays are senior citizen days!
imagine that! we could buy our very own senior citizen!
i'm not sure that's what the sign means...
sure it is! they probably have them all on racks and stuff so you can just browse through them and even try them on if you want.
try them on? i'm not sure that's legal.
legal, shmeegal. have you forgotten who you're talking to?
unfortunately no.

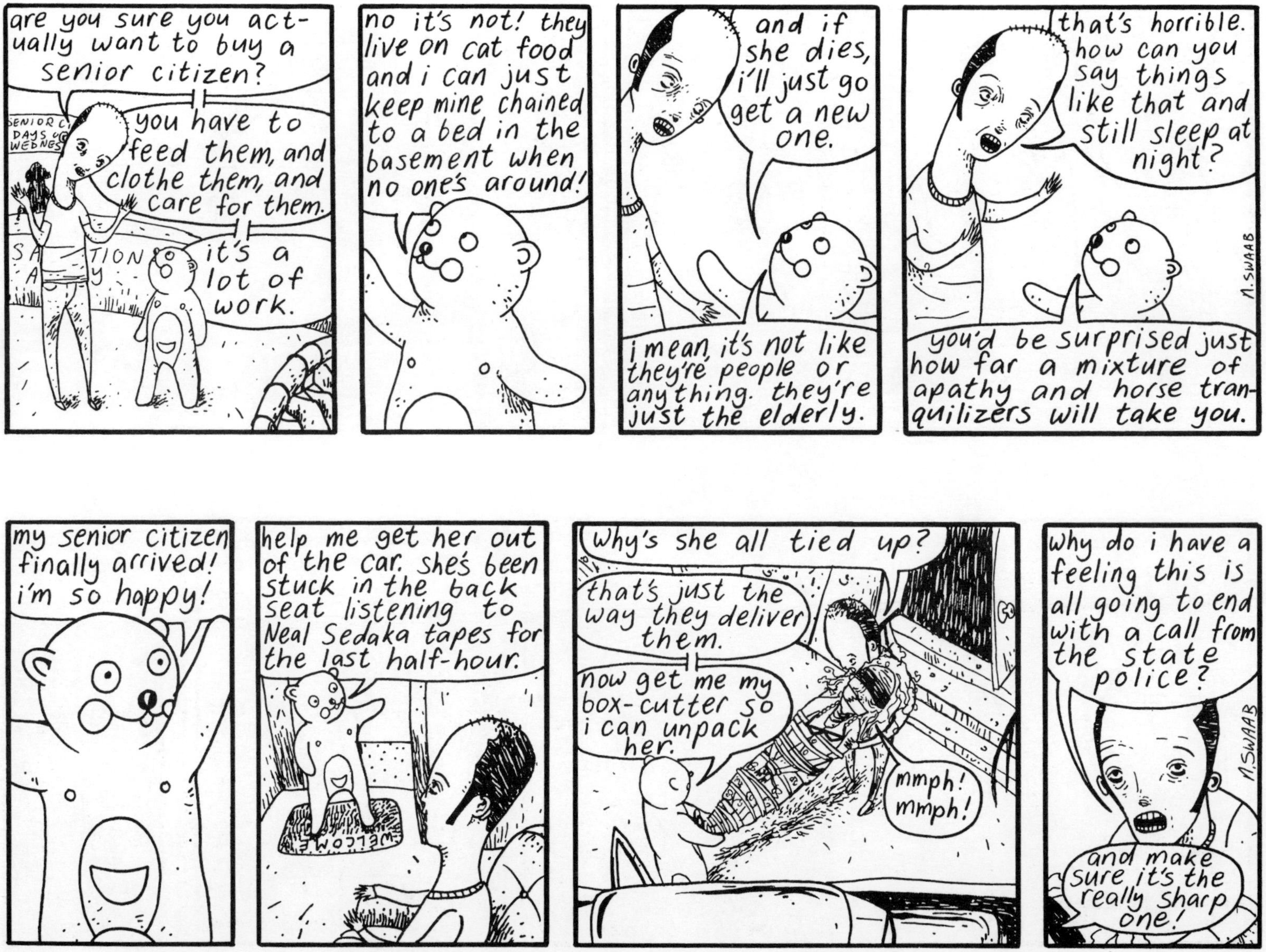
are you sure you actually want to buy a senior citizen?
you have to feed them, and clothe them, and care for them.
it's a lot of work.
no it's not! they live on cat food and i can just keep mine chained to a bed in the basement when no one's around!
and if she dies, i'll just go get a new one.
i mean, it's not like they're people or anything. they're just the elderly.
that's horrible. how can you say things like that and still sleep at night?
you'd be surprised just how far a mixture of apathy and horse tranquilizers will take you.
N. SWAAB
my senior citizen finally arrived! i'm so happy!
help me get her out of the car. she's been stuck in the back seat listening to Neal Sedaka tapes for the last half-hour.
why's she all tied up?
that's just the way they deliver them.
now get me my box-cutter so i can unpack her.
mmph! mmph!
why do i have a feeling this is all going to end with a call from the state police?
and make sure it's the really sharp one!
N. SWAAB

so, how's your senior citizen working out?
horrible. she shits herself constantly & i've had to pull her out of the bathtub twice 'cause she was too weak to do it herself.
so are you starting to regret your ill-fated purchase?
not really. she gives great blow-jobs. no teeth.
wow, it's just like "Harold & Maude" only without the love.
yeah, & my version includes donkey-punching.
M.SWAAB

god, my elderly woman is annoying. all she does is complain.
"i'm hungry! i'm thirsty! who are you!? untie me!"
nag, nag, nag...
so, what are you gonna do?
at first i was going to hook a car battery up to her nipples just to see what would happen,
but now i'm leaning more towards anal asphyxiation with a belt sander.
M.SWAAB
you do realize you're going to hell?
that's why i brought my swim-trunks.
what exactly is **that** supposed to mean?
i honestly have no idea...

hey, there's something wrong with my elderly woman. she's not moving anymore & she's colder than usual.
i think i broke her.
does she have a pulse?
no. what do you think that means?
it means we better go get some shovels & gasoline 'cause we've got a lot of digging to do & a lot of evidence to burn.
N. SWAAB
i can't believe my elderly woman's dead. it's such a shock.
well, she was 82, and you did starve her and chain her to a bed for 3 weeks straight.
oh yeah. i guess i did do that, didn't i? well, at least i learned a valuable lesson.
to love and cherish our elderly and treat them with the respect they deserve?
no. that they smell, and shit themselves, and tell boring stories that never end, and that i should avoid them like the plague because they're more trouble than they're worth.
somehow i think you've got a little more learning left to do.
N. SWAAB

Rehabilitating Mr. Wiggles

i'm looking for a girl who's sensitive, intelligent, witty, & honest. a girl to be my soul-mate.
VIDEO DATING
VIDEO DATING
or has really big knockers. i'm not too picky.
VIDEO DATING
M. SWAAB

your mom's like a potato chip.
how's that?
frito lay.
yeah, well your mom's like a bicycle.
how's that?
She likes to fuck a lot of random guys she doesn't know on a frequent basis, often for weeks at a time.
ouch.
M. SWAAB

hey, april fools! i've been using needles to poke holes in your condoms all year!
ha! the joke's on you!
i haven't needed to use them!
you're sad.
tell me about it.

the last time i got lucky was August 23rd, 1996.
i found a penny.

rehabilitating mr. wiggles presents:
true love
hey, honey, you know what i'm thinking about right now?
a roomfull of midgets fisting eachother to the tune of "Amazing Grace"?
yeah, how'd you know?
you complete me.
i should have never taken you to see Jerry McGuire.
isn't love great?
M.SWAAB
rehabilitating mr. wiggles presents:
subtle differences between guys & girls
guys.
hey, we have the same shirt.
wow. that's pretty cool. i guess we're shirt buddies.
girls.
you bitch! i bought that shirt first!
well, i slept with your boyfriend!
M.SWAAB

i took a girl back to my place last night.
she did things to my penis that would make a porn-star blush.
like dressing it up in a sailor's uniform and making it perform poorly written plays with home-made sock-puppets?
god, it was embarrassing.
N.SWAAB

i'm high on life!
and crystal-meth!
N.SWAAB

Rehabilitating Mr. Wiggles

since you're graduating, i just want to give you some words of wisdom my father gave to me when i was little.
if you scream i'll cut ya'! now do everything daddy says!
wow. that's fucked up.
he used to ride the dog to work.
N. SWAAB

someone asked me the other day if i wanted to have kids.
i did when i was younger, but now i'm not so sure.
well, you know how i feel about kids. i could take 'em or leave 'em.
©neil swaab 2000
and by "take 'em" you mean, "abduct them off the streets," and by "leave 'em" you mean "leave them broken and bloodied on the side of the road"?
tell anyone and i'll cut ya.
N. Swaab

you know, i once fucked a peach out of boredom.
who hasn't?
yeah, but i did it in a grocery store.
©neil swaab 2000
N. SWAAB

remember that time in Vienna? a certain restaurant? a certain coffee? a certain waiter?
©neil swaab 2000
Jean-Luc!!
shit. what did we do with his body?
i don't know. that's why i'm asking.
N. Swaab

my girlfriend just broke up with me. she said she wanted to be free to pursue her dream of fucking every other guy in the world that isn't me. i'm so sad.
so, what are you going to do?
©neil swaab 2000
i'm gonna drink till my eyes bleed!
but that's distilled turpentine.
even better!
N. SWAAB

i'm worried about you, neil. ever since your girl-friend broke-up with you, you've been de-pressed and dis-tant. i think it's starting to affect your work.
©neil swaab 2000
nonsense. my comics are just as funny as ever. take a look at my new one.
it's just a drawing of vaginas with pointy teeth and the phrase, "die, bitch! die!" re-peated over and over again.
yeah. pretty good, huh?
ummm...
just smile and nod and nobody gets hurt.
N. SWAAB

i just took the most wonderful shit.
©neil swaab 2000
it was quick, and smooth, and smelled like rose petals.
that's great! so, what's the problem?
i did it on the couch.
n. swaab

i'm sick of all these stupid horror movies coming out.
©neil swaab 2000
if people want to see something scary, they should just take a look at my last bowel movement. man, was that frightening.
are you aware you're fecally obsessed?
are you aware you're bald &have the genitals of a 5 year old boy?
didn't i tell you not to look in my dresser drawer?
n. swaab

Rehabilitating Mr. Wiggles

my grandmother used to tell me i looked like a young Tom Cruise.
that's when i knew she had a drinking problem.
i thought that was when she danced naked on a table at your bar-mitzvah, singing, "show me the money."
no, that's when i knew she had a tattoo of president Eisenhower on her buttocks.
she sounds like my kind of woman.
sometimes i wake up screaming and don't know why.
©neil swaab 2000
n. swaab

i think there's something wrong with my doctor. i went in for a sprained ankle and he asked to see my penis.
well, that's pretty common. most doctors will examine your genitals when you see them.
yeah, but with their mouths?
©neil swaab 2000
n. swaab

Neil Swaab

i think the cold weather is starting to affect people.
like yesterday i was wearing shorts and everyone was giving me dirty looks.
©neil swaab 2000
that's because your penis was hanging out of your zipper for half of the day.
hey, if you can think of a better way to show off a genital piercing, i'd like to know.
n. swaab

you know, you can't teach an old dog new tricks.
©neil swaab 2000
no, but you can set it on fire and watch it run frantically around the living room trying to put itself out.
that's just evil.
i'm sorry. i guess i should have interpreted your yelling, "burn, baby! burn!" as a sign of disapproval.
n. swaab

you know, you can lead a horse to water, but you can't make him drink.
you can if you have a few rolls of duct tape, a vaccuum pump, 4 feet of hosing, and a set of really menacing pliers.
your genius is both insightful and frightening.
©neil swaab 2000
n. swaab

nice rack!
thanks!
you have humungous boobs too.
©neil swaab 2000
n.swaab

of all the jobs i've had, working as a gynecologist was definitely my favorite.
looking up girls skirts on the subway doesn't make you a gynecologist.
hey, i was wearing a stethoscope.
©neil swaab 2000
n. swaab

you know what i discovered this afternoon?
little puppies do not like being kicked in the face.
excuse me?
oops. did i say "puppies"? i meant "children"?
what?
did i say "children"? i meant "logs". yeah, that's it. "logs".
logs don't have faces.
yeah, and they certainly don't scream as much either.
©neil swaab 2000
n. swaab

REHABILITATING
Mr. Wiggles
presents:
A LOVE POEM
©neil swaab 2000
I met her in a bar. Candy was her name. We spoke of old flames, new dreams, and women's gymnastics. she was the girl i'd been waiting for all my life.
Three pitchers of beer and an hour and a half later we were back at my place Doing what most horny adults do in the privacy of their own home:
Watching Spanish soap operas on Telemundo.
And then came the sex.
n.swaab
In the morning she was gone. So was my wallet. My stereo. My television.
In the end she left me with nothing but a broken heart and a burning sensation every time i pee.
Love hurts.
end.

i like to live each day like it was my last.
so how come you sit around all day in your underwear and never leave the apartment?
©neil swaab 2000
because i plan on dying alone, afraid, and naked in a pool of my own filth.
you're an uplifting man, neil, an uplifting man.
i'd kill myself if i could afford a gun.
n.swaab

New years is such a depressing time. hordes of drunken assholes scream incoherently at the top of their lungs, unaware of how pathetic their lives truly are as yet another wasted year ends and another, no-doubt, equally wasted year begins.
Whooo!
Ooow!
Brhghg!
©neil swaab 2000
people make resolutions to lose weight, end bad habits, and generally improve the quality of their lives only to forget these resolutions three months down the road when they're on their fifth tub of choco-chunky ice-cream, their third lung, and their last alimony payment.
fuck cancer. i need a drag.
girls hook up with guys they don't even like just for the sake of not being alone the moment the ball drops so they can have someone to kiss and pretend that just for that moment, they're not really alone.
under the right lighting, he's not that repulsive
i'm the king, baby.
and religious zealots take to the streets to spread their messages of urban enlightenment.
if you build it, They will come!
if you pray, He will come!
if you blow me, i will come!
n. swaab
next year, celebrate New years the Mr. Wiggles way. with some cheap whiskey, a cheap stripper, and a cheap sawed-off shotgun.
any of them celebratory assholes try to come in here and i'll blow their heads off.
happy holidays, kids

i had this friend a while back and we used to play the wildest pranks on each other.
©neil swaab 2000
like one night i snuck into his apartment while he slept and punched him in the throat.
but that doesn't sound like a prank- more like an unprovoked savage assault.
yeah... it was pretty funny...
n. swaab

Rehabilitating Mr. Wiggles

i'll have a low-fat ultra-super-carbonated protein chemical cleansing shake with extra laxative, please.
SUPER DRINK!
©neil swaab 2001
ugh. it seems like everybody's on a health kick these days. if they're not already vegetarians then they're on some crazy diet cooked up by yet another Hollywood has-been.
well, forget that. i mean, i **could** exercise and eat healthy and do all of that fun stuff that people who like their lives are prone to do. but when you think about it, the time they add to their lives is just going to come at the end, when they're too old and feeble to enjoy it anyway.
sure they'll squeeze in a few extra years, but those will probably be spent in some hospital bed soiled brown by their own feces & bodily secretions.
i say, "live fast, die young, and fuck everything that moves!"
and some things that don't, right?
now you've got it!
hey buddy, can you spare some change?
©neil swaab 2001
fucking dot-commers.

mr. wiggles, do you ever worry about penis size?
not really. **any** penis looks big to an eight year old's glossed-over, drugged-up eyes.
©neil swaab 2001
you scare me.
yeah, that's what **he** keeps saying.
n.swaab

your diet is appalling. your lack of physical activity is downright reckless. the only time i've ever seen you run was when you were being chased. by all accounts, you should be an obese, bed-ridden invalid.
©neil swaab 2001
how on earth do you stay so thin?
i just eat some raw meat and let the tape worms do the rest.
gee, that sounds kind of dangerous.
the anal bleeding means it's working.
n.swaab

Rehabilitating Mr. Wiggles

you woke me up this morning by punching me in the testicles.
©neil swaab 2001
you pasted naked pictures of my grandmother all over my bedroom.
you switched my apple juice with cat piss. and when i realized it was cat piss, you held me down and made me drink it anyway.
i think you're taking this April Fool's Day thing just a little too far.
it's April Fools day?
n. swaab

oh, **Dilbert**. you never cease to make me laugh.
reading the Sunday Comics, huh?
yeah. i had to stop reading the alternative weeklies for humor. you should **see** the filth they try and pass off as comic strips.
nothing but a bunch of **sicko's** obsessed with their own bodily functions and societal misfortunes.
i mean, we may live in a world of pain, suffering, and sexual depravity, but i don't want to read **jokes** about any of that stuff.
comics should be wholesome and stick to "safe" topics like how cute babies are or how mean people suck.
take this **Cathy** strip for instance. she can't seem to find a decent purse.
now **that's** the kind of good clean humor **every-one** should enjoy.
and it's edgy too.
or this **Garfield** strip where he professes his love of lasagna. pure genius.
it's funny 'cause he's a cat.
or any **Family Circus** comic. were we ever that innocent?
only in our dreams, mr. wiggles, only in our dreams...

you know how you keep encouraging me to relax and to release the things inside of me?
to open up and be forthcoming? to take what's inside and express it outwardly?
but most of all to release? always about the releasing?
you crapped on the couch again, didn't you?
and how!
©neil swaab 2001
n. swaab

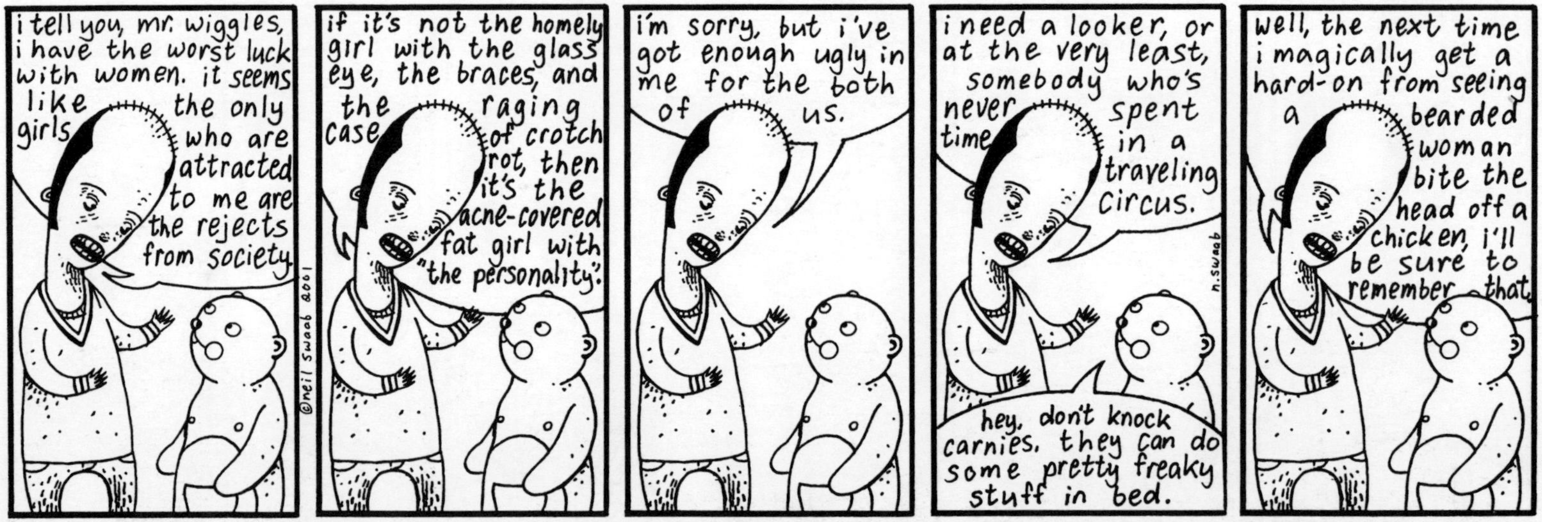
i tell you, mr. wiggles, i have the worst luck with women. it seems like the only girls who are attracted to me are the rejects from society.
if it's not the homely girl with the glass eye, the braces, and the raging case of crotch rot, then it's the acne-covered fat girl with "the personality".
i'm sorry, but i've got enough ugly in me for the both of us.
i need a looker, or at the very least, somebody who's never spent time in a traveling circus.
hey, don't knock carnies. they can do some pretty freaky stuff in bed.
well, the next time i magically get a hard-on from seeing a bearded woman bite the head off a chicken, i'll be sure to remember that.
©neil swaab 2001
n. swaab

Rehabilitating Mr. Wiggles

©neil swaab 2001
aw yeah...
n.swaab
every day is a good day...
...when you have a huge cock.

i used to think my life was miserable, but then i saw a boy with no arms or legs.
©neil swaab 2001
and then i started laughing hysterically.
it's the little things, you know...
they have special places in hell for bears like you.
as long as they're filled with limbless children to entertain me, i'm sure i'll be ok.
n.swaab

i love you.
gee, mr. wiggles, that's great. but there are so many different **kinds** of love.
©neil swaab 2001
i mean, there's the love a man has for a woman. or there's the love a man has for a friend. or even the love a man has for a good steak.
which kind is yours?
the kind where i secretly wipe my ass with all your socks and pretend not to know anything about it when you get a horrible foot disease.
i hate you, mr. wiggles,
have you ever loved something so much you had to kill it?
n.swaab

REHABILITATING
Mr. Wiggles
presents:
CATS ARE CUTE
©neil swaab 2001
it's been a whole **five minutes** since i last licked my asshole.
it **must** be dirty again.
man, that is one tasty cat asshole...
gee, all of a sudden i don't feel so—
hrrgghgh!
hmmm... ass-vomit...
n.swaab
oh yeah, that's the sweet, sweet stuff...
slrp... slrp...

Rehabilitating Mr. Wiggles

would you like some of my "special" brownies?
sure!
©neil swaab 2001
wait a second! there's no pot in these brownies!
what, exactly, makes them so special?
let's just say there's a little bit of me in everything i make.
if they weren't so refreshingly delicious, i'd be beyond myself with disgust.
n. swaab

♫ la dee ♪ ♫ da... ♫
ooh! a cat!
lick. lick.
©neil swaab 2001
it sure would be funny if i kicked the crap out of it.
wait a second... what would **Jesus** do?
i'd kick its face in!
i can do **anything** and just forgive myself **afterwards!**
i'm **Jesus**, for God's sakes!
wow! thanks, Jesus!
make that fucker bleed!
n. swaab

i became an artist to get girls, but the only thing i ever got was a raging case of carpel-tunnel syndrome. art sucks.
still, you must be pretty happy. you're living your dream.
©neil swaab 2001
i don't know. somehow my dream involved a lot more money and a lot more nudity. right now i'm flat broke and the only boobs i see are the ones that are slowly growing on my chest. and what the hell am i supposed to do with those?
i'll give you five dollars if you let me touch them.
make it six and i'll giggle like a horny school-girl!
n. swaab

Jesus, why is there so much suffering in the world?
because without pain there can be no pleasure.
©neil swaab 2001
why do bad things happen to good people?
the same reason movie sequals are guaranteed to suck. it's all part of God's plan, my child.
Jesus, how come i can only see you after i've been huffing aerosol for hours on end?
'cause that shit fucks you up like nobody's business.
i can smell colors.
n. swaab

Rehabilitating Mr. Wiggles

it's finally friday! time to relax. the weekends are all about letting go.
i just farted!
©neil swaab 2001
exactly! why contain ourselves? we should be free to be men! **real** men!
i shouldn't have forced it though. it smells like the plague.
it smells like freedom!
i have freedom running down the side of my leg.
you can't stop a revolution!
can i at least wash it off?
n.swaab
it seems like all i do is work and work and work and never accomplish **anything**.
©neil swaab 2001
i've got no life, no job, no girl. no food.
the only thing i have is the freedom to walk around on a nice summer's day.
why can't life be easy?
it is. you're just not very good at it.
n.swaab

Jesus, who's your favorite Backstreet Boy?
i have no favorites. everyone is equal in the eyes of the lord.
it's Justin, isn't it? he's dreamy.
Justin's in 'N Sync.
what about Drew?
he's in 98°.
erik?
O-Town.
Jesus, how come you know so much about Boy Bands?
i'm...uh... omniscient.
i had a friend who was "omniscient" back in college. but he was just experimenting.
hey!
relax, Jesus. i'm just fucking with you.

REHABILITATING
Mr. Wiggles presents:
Lepers in Love
your touch makes my skin burn.
i think that's the disease.
i crave you. your sores are like a piece of chewy heaven.
when i'm with you, it's like the whole world is rotting. and not just us.
let me nibble on your ear.
i left it in the car.
then, please, have mine.
you complete me...literally.

Rehabilitating Mr. Wiggles

you know, life is a gift.
©neil swaab 2001
can i return it?
n.swaab

summer fresh! mmm... so soft and comfy!
hey, you're not our **usual** laundry bear. where's Snuggy, the **Snuggy's** bear?
©neil swaab 2001
he's...uh...**sick.** yeah, that's it. he had a bad burrito and he's shitting his brains out somewhere.
in the meantime, Snuggy wanted **me** to fill in for him. i'm Mr. Wiggles.
you smell like cheap whiskey and cigarettes.
are **you** going to help us do laundry?
umm...kind of. i was thinking we could play a special laundry game; a **secret** game. say, your parents aren't home, are they?
huh?
oh, never mind. so, do you want to play?
ok!
ow, Mr. Wiggles! doing laundry hurts!
i used to play this game with daddy!
n.swaab

Neil Swaab

...and that's why God invented penicillin.
eww...
mr. wiggles, what are you doing with these kids!? you **know** you're not allowed to associate with minors.
that's just one federal judge's **opinion**.
besides, i'm teaching them to **read**.
you're teaching kids to read?
well, i thought i'd give back to the community.
i don't believe it. the only thing you've **ever** given to the community is a rampant strain of **syphilis**. what's in it for **you**?
well, you know how i love children.
that's what bothers me.
relax. what trouble could i **possibly** get into teaching kids to read?
hmm... well i **suppose** you're right. i guess i'll leave you alone then.
great.
now, where were we?
ANAL INTRUDER monthly
mr. wiggles, what's a "Cleveland Steamer"?
let's turn to page 43 and find out!

oh how i hate summer. it's hot as hell in here.
yeah, and it smells like the devil's asshole.
we've **got** to get air conditioning.
or at least not leave week-old burritos out to roast in the heat.
those aren't burritos, they're the three pairs of underwear i've already sweated through today.
my balls are on **fire**!
eeeww... i ate one of them this afternoon.
really? how'd it taste?
like a holocaust.
now, if you'll excuse me, i'm going to go vomit until i pass out.

Rehabilitating Mr. Wiggles

IT'S YOUR BIRTHDAY!
PIG OUT!
©neil swaab 2001
ugh. who the hell comes up with this crap?
probably mental patients. or housewives constrained to bed-rest.
IT'S YOUR BIRTHDAY! PIG OUT!
this is ridiculous. it shouldn't be this hard to find a decent birthday card; after-all, look at this selection!
yet, every card either has some half-retarded talking animal on it, some cheesy "over-the-hill" metaphor, or is so sentimental and mushy it makes me want to vomit!
i mean, look at this card! what the hell does "the morning of our love" even mean!?
the morning of our love transcends all...
this is the kind of card you give to somebody who's dying!
excuse me, can i help you?
yes, do you have any cards that don't suck?
sure! have you seen this hilarious one?
it's a duck playing the banjo!
HERE'S TO YOU... ...DUCKEY
lady, don't push me.
n.swaab
everybody wants to change the world. well, i want to change the world too. but not for the better.
©neil swaab 2001
i want to make the world a worse place.
i want to throw my bottles into the ocean and dump my waste onto helpless animals.
i want to give crack to babies and then sell them to cults for human sacrifices.
i want to punch blind people in the head and pretend that someone else did it.
i want to ride the elderly like horses through the streets of New York!
i want to break into people's houses when they're not there, crap on their floors, and leave a note saying, "wake up, America! it's poo-ing time!"
in fact, that will be my new slogan when i run for president!
and, if elected, i'll pass a law requiring that John Travolta stars in every film! and when the country is tired and broken and pleading for an end to the insanity, Vice President Travolta and i will turn to the people, in our matching white polyester suits, and say...
..."look who's talking now, bitch!"
oh, Mr. Wiggles, will you ever be rehabilitated?
why, what's so wrong with me?
n.swaab

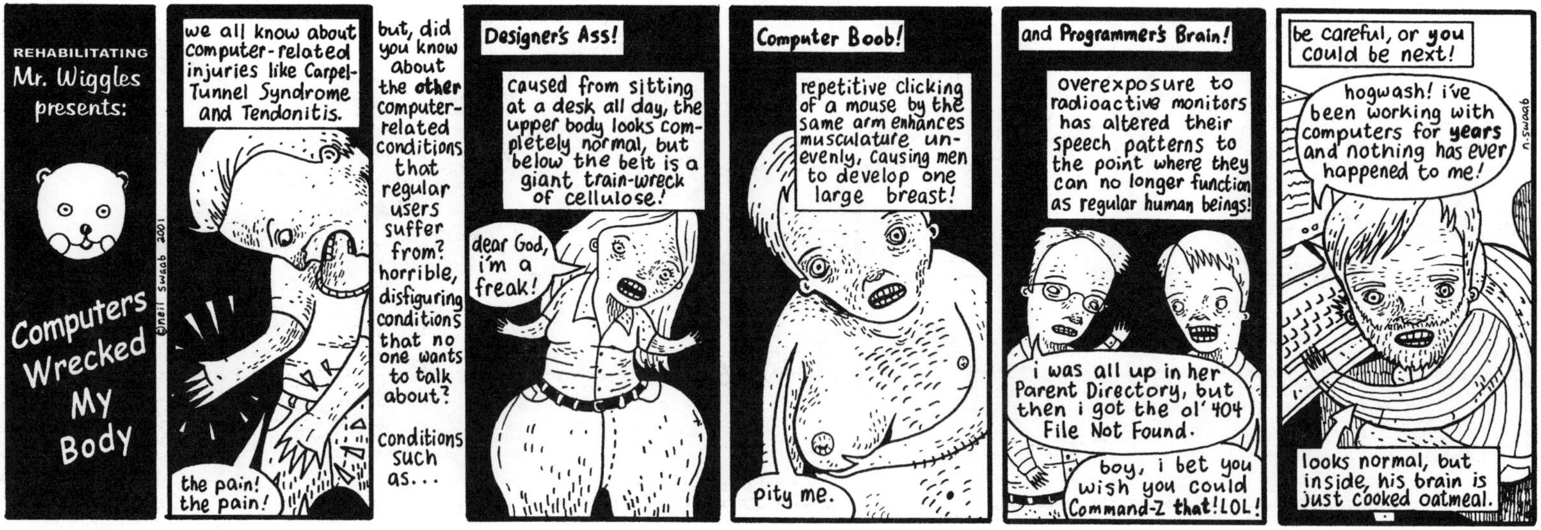
REHABILITATING
Mr. Wiggles presents:
Computers Wrecked My Body
©neil swaab 2001
we all know about computer-related injuries like Carpel-Tunnel Syndrome and Tendonitis.
the pain! the pain!
but, did you know about the other computer-related conditions that regular users suffer from? horrible, disfiguring conditions that no one wants to talk about?
conditions such as...
Designer's Ass!
caused from sitting at a desk all day, the upper body looks completely normal, but below the belt is a giant train-wreck of cellulose!
dear God, i'm a freak!
Computer Boob!
repetitive clicking of a mouse by the same arm enhances musculature unevenly, causing men to develop one large breast!
pity me.
and Programmer's Brain!
overexposure to radioactive monitors has altered their speech patterns to the point where they can no longer function as regular human beings!
i was all up in her Parent Directory, but then i got the ol' 404 File Not Found.
boy, i bet you wish you could Command-Z that! LOL!
be careful, or you could be next!
hogwash! i've been working with computers for years and nothing has ever happened to me!
looks normal, but inside, his brain is just cooked oatmeal.
n.swaab

i'm so excited! now that the new TV season is starting, i actually have a reason to get out of bed in the morning!
©neil swaab 2001
once again i can watch fresh, original programming!
like my favorite courtroom drama! you know, the one that you can tell is really good because they're always yelling?
ooh, and that comedy about the group of twenty-somethings with the wacky neighbor who get into those kooky situations!
and let's not forget about that one with the non-traditional family where the father always manages to screw things up!
hell, the only show i'm looking forward to even more is that drama where the teenagers deal with really mature issues!
unless, of course, we're talking about reality programs or game-shows, in which case, i can't wait for new episodes of that one they adapted from England!
yes, you can bet i'll be glued to my television this Fall!
you know, all this TV watching can't be good for your social life.
with innovative shows like those to stimulate my brain, who needs one?
n.swaab

Rehabilitating Mr. Wiggles

n. swaab

thank you, Christina Aguillera. thank you Jennifer Lopez. thank you, Keanu Reeves...
what are you doing there, Mr. Wiggles?
©neil swaab 2001
thanking my lucky stars that i'm alive.
throw in David Hasselhoff for me.
n. swaab

REHABILITATING
Mr. Wiggles
presents:
Secret Confessions
©neil swaab 2001
i like to talk with an English accent on the phone. it makes me feel more intelligent.
i sometimes fart in public and blame it on small children.
watching old women swimming sexually excites me.
i jerk-off to Sesame Street.
i once found a piece of poo on the ground and ate it! and, God help me, i liked it!
i think Stone Phillips is a handsome man!
we're horrible people!
hold me!
n.swaab

oh, mr. wiggles, i'm so hungry. i sure wish we had some food.
why did you have to spend all our money on crack?
©neil swaab 2001
i didn't spend it **all** on crack. what was left i donated to a homeless shelter for abused children.
really?
uh-huh.
nah, i'm just kidding. i spent it all on crack.
n.swaab

Rehabilitating Mr. Wiggles

Mr. Wiggles, why does my no-no spot get all tingly and start to grow when i think about naked Barbie dolls?
well Timmy, that's called an erection. when your body receives certain physical or mental stimuli, your penis becomes engorged with blood, causing it to swell and elongate in anticipation of sexual intercourse
©neil swaab 2001
gee Mr. Wiggles, that sounds scary.
i wouldn't worry about it, Timmy. erections are nothing to be afraid of.
so i shouldn't be concerned that you have one poking against the back of my leg?
you ask too many questions, Timmy. perhaps a full-body massage would put your mind at ease.
n.swaab
maybe it's my changing, pre-pubescent body or the fact that you violently assaulted me, but i'm still **terrified** of erections.
oh, Timmy, don't be so dramatic. it was a loving, **caring** forced sodomy– the handcuffs and throat gag were for your **protection**.
©neil swaab 2001
that may be, but i'm still petrified of the darn things. they're always coming up on the bus ride to school or when Mrs. Spencer bends over to pick up a piece of chalk or whenever i watch professional wrestling on TV. and i have these terrible **urges**!
you're making too much of this, Timmy. trust me, erections are your friend.
i don't know, Mr. Wiggles. i've never wanted to rub any of my friends **raw** with my bare hands or shove them into a jar of warm mayonnaise before.
really? i guess we must hang with a different crowd.
n.swaab

they've used our **transportation** against us! they've used our **mail** against us! what's **next**!?
they're going to violate our most treasured, honored asset now. they're going to use our **Boy Bands** against us!
subliminal messages urging a violent revolt will be hidden in all of the Backstreet Boys new videos!
did A.J. just say, "Kill the capitalist swine?
shh... hypnotized by swaying buttocks and choreographed street moves. must assasinate political leaders...
©neil swaab 2001
the members of 'N Sync will be injected with a special strain of walking Anthrax transmitted only through live performances of their unique pop music!
i don't care if kissing you causes my inner organs to melt; i'll always love you, Justin!
it's the fans that **really** count!
actual Timberlake Anthrax spores!
98° will be turned into human boy bombs!
look out! if their songs go above complete mediocrity, they're gonna blow!
if you think **that's** bad, just wait until they turn our **female** sensations against us!
n.swaab
J-Lo's ass requires the blood of a thousand dead soldiers to feed its cravings! now go, my minions, into the night! go! **bwah! ha! ha!**
like they keep saying, this is a war unlike any we've ever fought before. God help us all!

i just started this new job. it's nice and all, but, man, i **hate** being the new guy.
©neil swaab 2001
you never know **what** you're doing, **where** you're going, or who **anybody** is.
everyone looks at you funny. and they ask these **stupid** questions, too. you know, like, "what's your background?", "where are you from?", "why are you naked?", "will you get that thing out of my face?"
got fired already, huh?
like **they've** never seen a man type without using his **hands** before.
n.swaab

what are **you** thankful for this Thanksgiving?
©neil swaab 2001
genetic cloning!
fake id's!
that i'm no longer chained to a water heater in the basement!
XXX LOCO DRINK XXX
and that leather handcuffs leave no visible signs of bruising!
happy Thanksgiving!
hrgh!
n.swaab

Jesus, who put the "bomp" in the "bomp sh' bomp sh' bomp"? was it you?
nope. sorry.
©neil swaab 2001
who put the "ram" in the "ramma lamma ding dong"?
that's something every man must discover for themselves.
Jesus, who put their penis in my mouth while i was sleeping?
my friend, Tony. he's got problems.
my mouth tastes like man-sack.
n.swaab

welcome back to STD Jeopardy...
...the only game show about STD's played by people with STD's!
©neil swaab 2001
Jim, you're in the lead. what'll it be?
9000
JIM
450
SARAH
well, this may be my syphilitic brain talking, but i'm going to take "feel the burn" for $600.
ooh! a daily double!
feel the burn
scratch n' sniff
what's that smell?
200
400
600
800
often caused by Chlamydia, this STD is characterized by a yellow or white drip from the penis or discharge or burning in the vagina.
what is nongonococcal urethritis?
correct! wow, Jim, you're on fire!
nah, that's just my genitals. i'll take "name that discharge" for $200.
ah, good ol' TV...
n.swaab
it's fun and educational!
this one is a picture clue!

how did you sleep last night?
like a baby.
©neil swaab 2001
i crapped myself in the middle of the night and woke up every two hours crying for my mommy.
n.swaab

Rehabilitating Mr. Wiggles

dating sure has changed. you have to be careful these days– you never know **what** a woman might have.
well, i don't have to worry about that with **my** girlfriend.
©neil swaab 2001
why's that?
because she's imaginary.
you're pathetic.
she's real if you believe.
n.swaab

HONK! HONK!
hey! Mr. Wiggles! come on out!
what's all that noise?
mph! mph!
©neil swaab 2001
Jesus?
hey man, check out my sweet-ass ride. i've wanted one of these all my life. figured you only turn 2002 years old once, you know. decided to splurge.
who are all these girls?
oh, these are my new lady friends.
i call them the "Jiggle Sisters."
we're going to get tattoos and then get shit-faced drunk to celebrate the ol' B-day. wanna come?
yeah, but i'm kind of... uh... tied up right now.
yeah, yeah. i hear ya. alright. your loss, man.
come on, ladies. let's go dance with the snake!
oh, J-Man! you're the coolest!
running with the devil...
hey, what'd i tell you about touching the hair!
holy mid-life crisis!
n.swaab

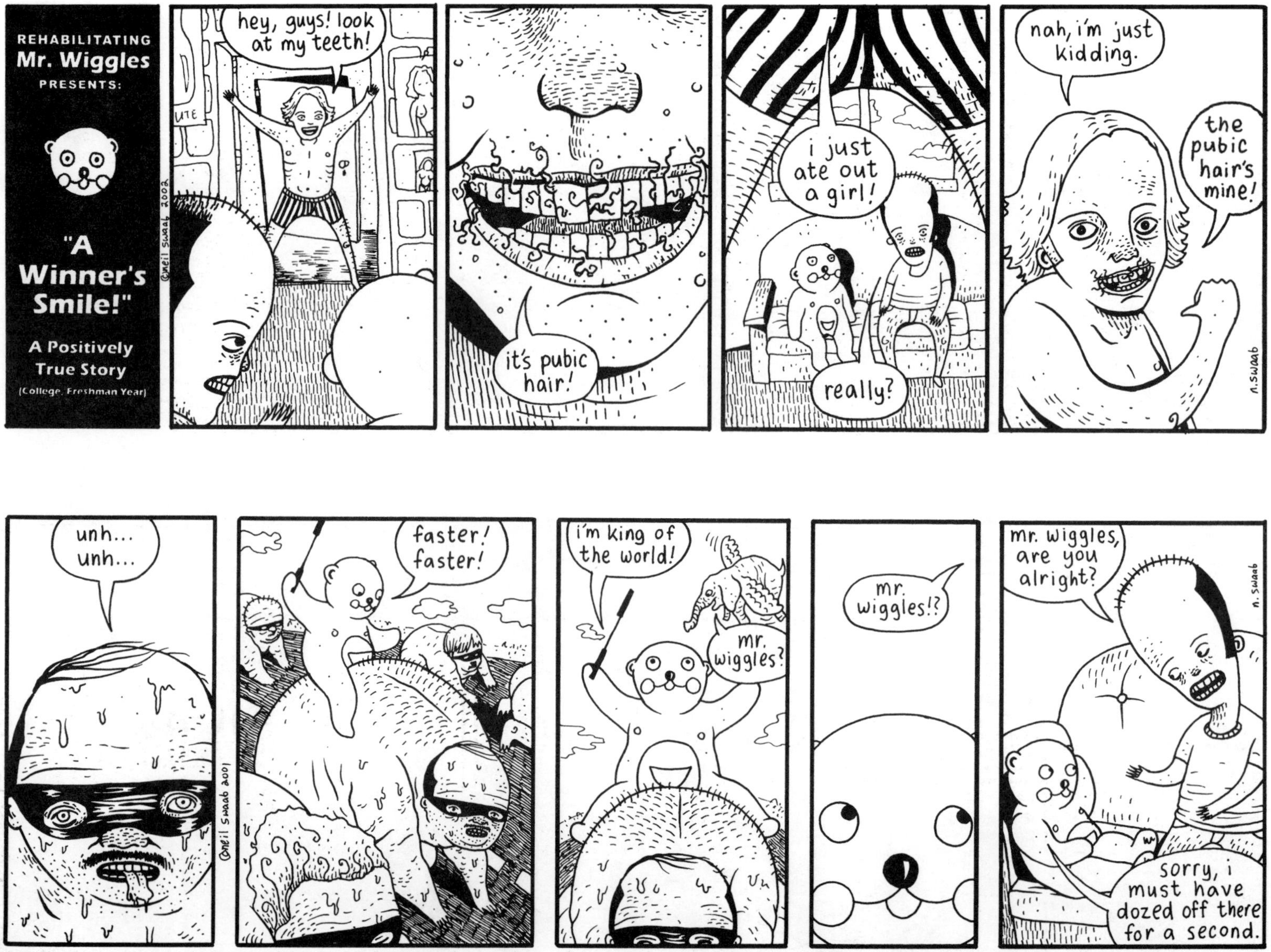
REHABILITATING
Mr. Wiggles
PRESENTS:
"A Winner's Smile!"
A Positively True Story
(College, Freshman Year)
hey, guys! look at my teeth!
©neil swaab 2002
it's pubic hair!
i just ate out a girl!
really?
nah, i'm just kidding.
the pubic hair's mine!
n. swaab
unh... unh...
©neil swaab 2001
faster! faster!
i'm king of the world!
mr. wiggles?
mr. wiggles!?
mr. wiggles, are you alright?
n. swaab
sorry, i must have dozed off there for a second.

...and **that's** how you can cure a simple yeast infection with just a bottle of soda and a AA battery.
ick.
KNOCK! KNOCK!
say, do you hear that?
©Neil Swaab 2002
what? that repetitive knocking sound?
yeah. it's coming from the door. i think we have a visitor.
wait a second. you haven't done anything i should know about, have you?
MR. WIGGLES' CRACK STAND
AAAH!
REFRESHING!
mmm.. crack!
All the crack you can stomach
10¢
crack! get your crack here! c'mon kids! first-timer's special, 10¢!
uh... nothing i can think of.
well, we're not expecting anyone. i wonder who that could be...
n. swaab
don't **you**?
yes, don't you? isn't that the question we're all asking these days? well, join us next week for the continuation of a brand new story-line where we'll answer such hair-raising questions as: "who is at the door?" "what do they want?" and "where do they come from?" oh, it's almost too much to bear! i think i'm going to be...oh yeah, i'm definitely going to be sick! blrgghhh!!!

hello, Neil.
©Neil Swaab 2001
look, old man, i'm not giving any handouts this week.
first those girl scout whores and then the friggin' needy. it's enough to—
hey, wait a second. how do you know my name?
don't you recognize me, Neil? i'm **you** from the **future**.
holy Jesus! i look like shit!
i've traveled a long way across space and time to meet you.
what for?
is it to give me a message or warn me of some terrible danger or help me win the lottery or something?
no. i've come to give you this gun.
n. swaab
kill yourself. trust me, you have nothing to live for.

my life in the future can't be **so** bad that i'd need to travel back in time to convince me to kill myself.
i mean, i must have **some** reason to live.
©neil swaab 2002
after working for so many years, i'll bet i've at least got a decent job, huh?
hardly. you know that guy who cleans up elephant shit at the zoo?
that's me? well, i suppose it's not **that** bad.
you suck his dick for money.
n.swaab

hey, Future-Me, how'd you get those horrible burns on your hands?
©neil swaab 2002
let me guess: was it working in some Martian coal mines? or living underneath a radioactive sun?
or, ooh! i know! battling inter-stellar aliens hell-bent on taking over our neo-futurist utopia?
let me put it this way: you need to get a girlfriend. fast.
n.swaab

Rehabilitating Mr. Wiggles

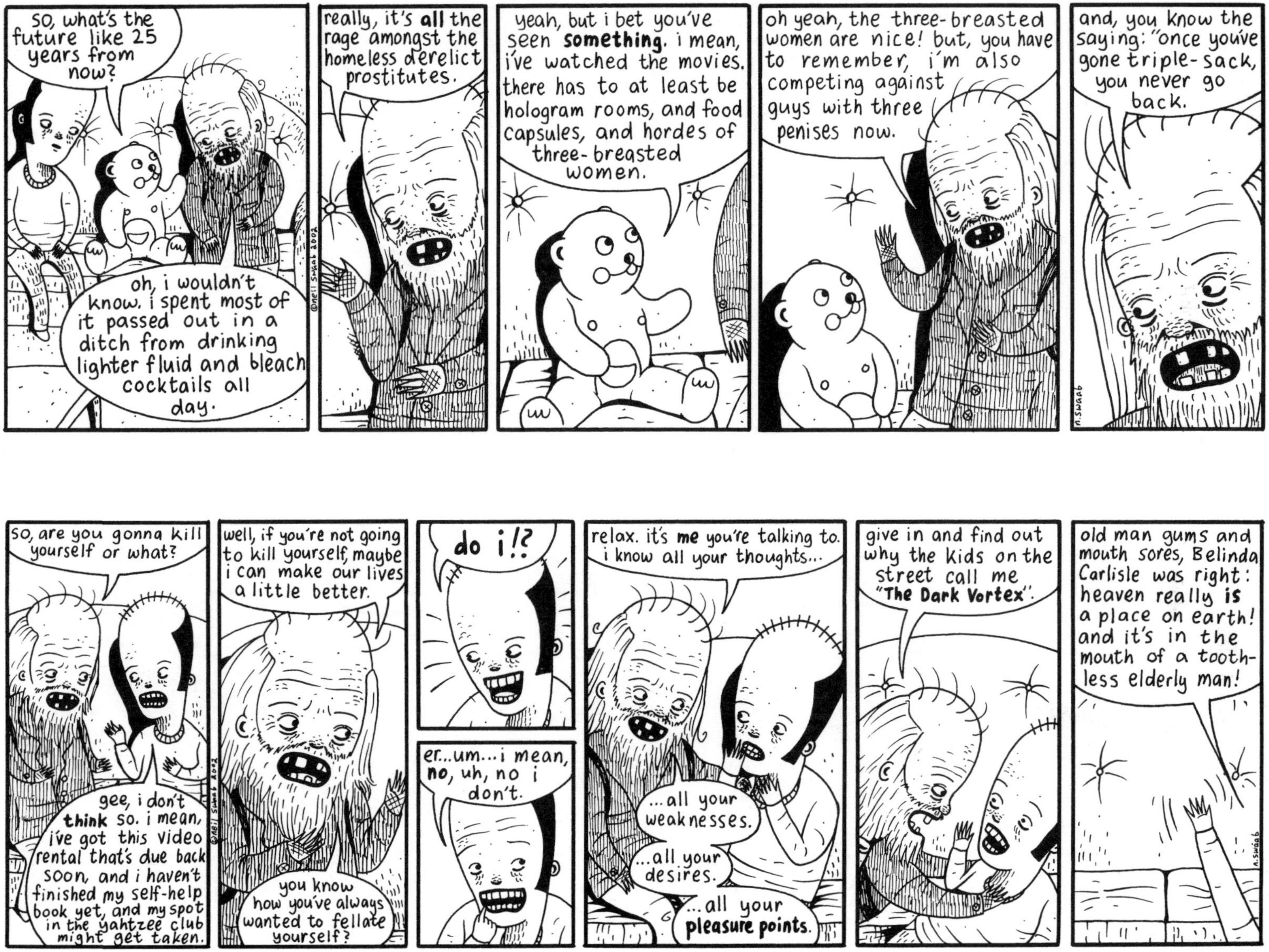

so, what's the future like 25 years from now?
oh, i wouldn't know. i spent most of it passed out in a ditch from drinking lighter fluid and bleach cocktails all day.
©neil swaab 2002
really, it's **all** the rage amongst the homeless derelict prostitutes.
yeah, but i bet you've seen **something**. i mean, i've watched the movies. there has to at least be hologram rooms, and food capsules, and hordes of three-breasted women.
oh yeah, the three-breasted women are nice! but, you have to remember, i'm also competing against guys with three penises now.
and, you know the saying: "once you've gone triple-sack, you never go back.
n.swaab
so, are you gonna kill yourself or what?
gee, i don't **think** so. i mean, i've got this video rental that's due back soon, and i haven't finished my self-help book yet, and my spot in the yahtzee club might get taken.
©neil swaab 2002
well, if you're not going to kill yourself, maybe i can make our lives a little better.
you know how you've always wanted to fellate yourself?
do i!?
er...um...i mean, **no**, uh, no i don't.
relax. it's **me** you're talking to. i know all your thoughts...
...all your weaknesses.
...all your desires.
...all your **pleasure points**.
give in and find out why the kids on the street call me **"The Dark Vortex"**.
old man gums and mouth sores, Belinda Carlisle was right: heaven really **is** a place on earth! and it's in the mouth of a toothless elderly man!
n.swaab

i can't believe i'm being orally gratified by a future version of myself.
slrrp. slrrp. smack. suck.
©neil swaab 2002
so, does this make me gay?
yes.
hey, wait a second! aren't you supposed to say something witty or insightful about how it doesn't?
lick. slrrp. suck.
hello...?
slrrp. slrrp. mmm...
n.swaab
oh, Jesus! oh, Jesus! i'm gonna... i'm gonna...
©neil swaab 2002
oh, Jesus!
yo, wassup! somebody called my—
ah gross! my eyes! i'm blind! i'm blind! yech!
n. swaab

Rehabilitating Mr. Wiggles

something feels wrong, Mr. Wiggles.
i think having hot, deviant man-on-man action for an obscene amount of time with the future version of myself has caused a rift in the space-time continuum, altering the very fabric of life itself.
ya think?
©neil swaab 2002
well, all i know is that when i woke up this morning, my genitals looked like something out of a slasher film and have been leaking a rainbow of fluids, pusses, and discharges all day.
so it's either that, or i've got the worst STD in all of human history.
well, you **did** have relations with a homeless elderly prostitute who's survived off a diet of nothing but alcohol and man-meat the past twenty years.
and Ockham's razor **would** suggest the simplest explanation.
oh you— always with Ockham's razor...
n.swaab
what the hell, Future-Me? you said you'd give me the ride of my life. you never said anything about giving me an STD the likes of which Stephen King could base a novel.
what gives?
©neil swaab 2002
hmmm... must have slipped my mind. and it's a shame too since, although cripplingly disfiguring, this STD from the future **is** easily cured.
the only problem, however, is that the cure won't be discovered for another fifteen years. pity.
but i'm in agony **now**!
well, you **could** always kill yourself and end our suffering.
i knew it! you never gave up on trying to drive me to suicide!
and i thought you loved me.
ha! how can i love **you** when i can't even love **myself**? no, the only thing i love is the sweet smell of crumpled dollar bills torn from sweaty, probing hands in exchange for sexual favors to help drown out the unrelenting hell that is human existence.
that and puppy dogs in party hats. they're just so cute.
well, naturally...
n.swaab

you know, Mr. Wiggles, Future-Me said that he was unable to love because he couldn't love himself. i think all we need to do is lift his self-esteem and he'll stop trying to drive me to suicide.
well, **that** doesn't sound very fun.
©neil swaab 2002
how about we just point over his shoulder and say, "hey! look over there!" and when he turns, jab him in the throat with an ice-pick and be all like, "what's up **now**, mutha'-fucka'? huh? you wanna step? huh? yeah, that's what i **thought**, beeyatch."
and then we down a couple 40's, get some mad ho's over here, and party all night. word.
oh, alright. we'll do it **your** way.
pussy.
n. swaab

you are one **smokin'** old man. if we were alone, i'd play a game of "connect-the-dots" with all the liver spots on your body.
using my tongue.
i wanna celebrate you!
©neil swaab 2002
living on the streets hasn't sullied your image. why, the stench of urine and feces is almost **unnoticable** after you get used to it.
it's a heavenly scent, like smelling God's asshole.
looks and personality aren't **everything**. you've got that **undescribable** quality that so many people would kill for.
people are **drawn** to you. sorta' like when Mr. Wiggles lit that mime on fire. only with less screaming.
you're uplifting. seeing how pathetic you are makes me feel better about my life.
the kids on the street might call you "The Dark Vortex," but i call you "My Sunbeam of Joy".
now get the hell out of here before i chew your balls off.
he'll do it too. he's short and fast and has teeth like razors.
n. swaab

well guys, you've managed to lift my withered spirits. it's time i returned home.
whatever.
seriously, don't let the door hit ya.
for my journey into the past has come to an end, as all journeys must. but, perhaps, the **real** journey was in **here** all along.
great. fantastic. stupendous.
zzzz...
afterall, isn't it in our own hearts that we—
Slam!
whew! thank God **he's** gone. one of you is **more** than enough for me.
who can take that much **whining**?
i'll say!
but i think i've learned something from this experience. seeing my future self has taught me that i've got to make a few changes. it's time i started **living** my life instead of **hiding** from it.
click.
no more sleeping in until 4:00 in the afternoon. no more wasting my days away in front of the TV. no more endless procrastinating until i find my life has **vanished** before my very eyes. i need to take action now!
hey, Maury Povich has those morbidly obese babies on TV again! wanna watch?
do you have to ask?
but if you **don't** have sex with me and my friend in the bathroom stall, then the terrorists **win**.
n. swaab

it's like, the things you want, you know, you just can't have. or, i mean, you never get 'em, right?
i hear ya, brother.
©neil swaab 2002
and then there's like these women. and they look so pretty and smell so nice. and it's like, "what's up?", you know. but they're all like, "i'll tell you what's not up. you, man. you."
i like the ones with the big thingies the best.
and then there's like, sideburns, you know what i'm saying? like, when i started growing 'em i thought, "yeah, man. yeah." but like, they're not all fun and games. they're a responsibility. they'll outgrow you if you let them.
you gotta take care of 'em, you know. you gotta be fuckin' vigilant.
yeah. put the smackdown on the burns.
fuckin' sideburns.
fuckin' women.
fuckin' basic human wants and desires.
fuck.
yeah, you're definitely not "a drinker".
n. swaab

yeah, i know i screwed up big time. i let all those Catholic priests touch your kiddies in their swimtrunk areas.
and now the whole organization's gone to shit. unless we get some fresh blood, this religion's going to go the way of the dinosaurs.
©neil swaab 2002
so it's time to change this whole religion thing around – shake things up a little! join the MTV generation!
the new Catholicism's going to be young! and fresh! and hip! not like those damn Budhists who can all blow me!
check this out: from now on, Catholic priests are allowed to marry! not only that, they can have the freakiest sexcapades they want!
gangbangs!? cornholing!? donkey-punching!? who cares!? it's all good with me! as long as it's over eighteen years old, they can stick their dicks in anything!
also, i'm wiping out everybody's sins from the 1980's!
look, we all did shit in the '80's we'd like to forget – the J-Man included – so let's do just that! forget about it! hey, it worked for Burt Reynolds, why not us!?
and listen to this: starting in June, every Thursday night is Ladies' Night! Ladies can sin all they want and pay no penance!
and if you show us your boobs, you get free Margaritas!
so come on back to Catholicism: where the good times never end, the drinks are always overflowing, and our priests won't mouth-rape your children anymore!
n. swaab

Rehabilitating Mr. Wiggles

spank it! lick it! stick it in it! i've been a bad, little girl...
jesus christ, mr. wiggles! are you watching child porn again!?
©neil swaab 2001
relax, it's just MTV.
wow. they'll really do **anything** for ratings, huh? i remember when they used to play **music**. now it's just teenagers in their underwear straddling poles.
yeah, it's much better.
I don't know. somehow seeing underage girls dressed in next to nothing, gyrating, singing sexually suggestive lyrics, and rolling around on lavish sets gives me a really funny feeling.
yes, it's called an erection.
now pass the lube and stop talking. i'm trying to concentrate.
eww...
n.swaab

it's interesting just how much sex and religion are tied together.
©neil swaab 2001
for instance, did you know there are certain spiritual masters who spend lifetimes learning how to channel built up sexual energy and can orgasm without touching themselves even once?
yeah, i can do that too. it's called "premature ejaculation".
and it's not so spiritual when you do it in your pants during a rerun of "Blossom" on The Family Channel.
Mayim Bialik?
don't judge me.
n.swaab

'sup.
this is your brain.
whoah man, it's like everything is tied together, you know, like why are we here? what does life mean? can thoughts really hurt?
this is your brain on drugs.
what are you looking at!? nobody understands me! i don't need you! i don't need anybody!
this is your brain on alcohol.
yee-haw! i'm a cowboy!
this is your brain on a miniature pony.
what are you doing in here!? stop following me! get out! get out!
this is your brain on the toilet.
any questions?
what the hell was that commercial about?
i don't know, but i'm never doing drugs again... this week.
n.swaab

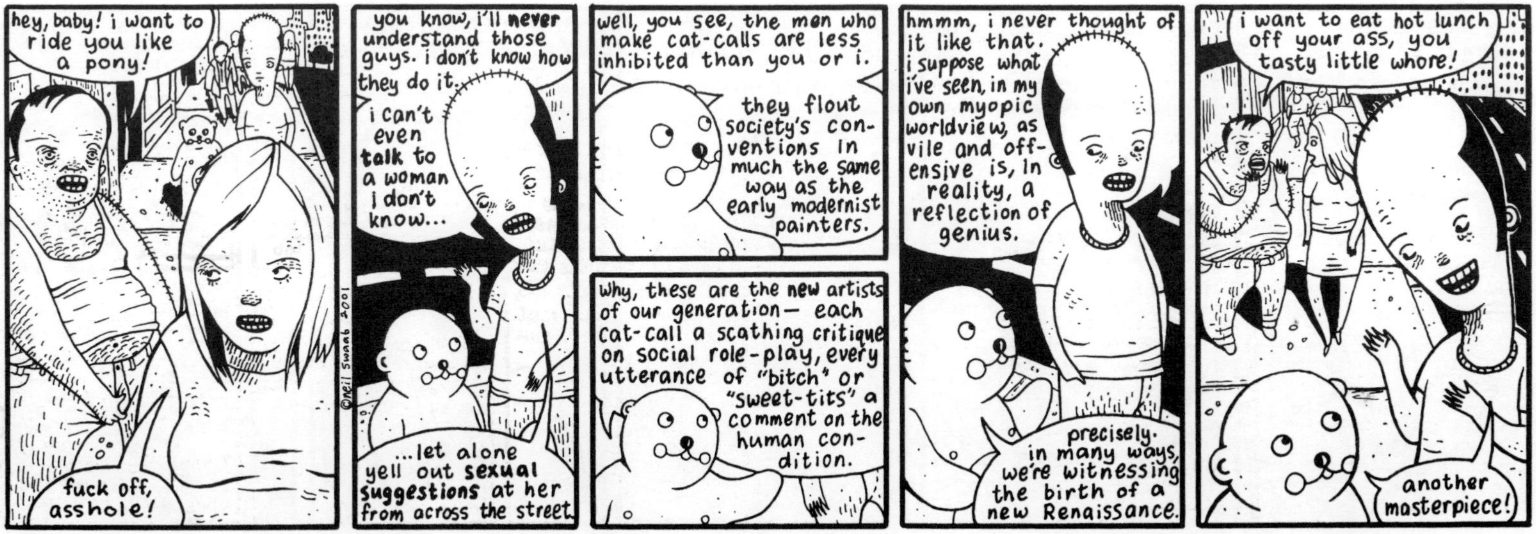
hey, baby! i want to ride you like a pony!
fuck off, asshole!
©neil swaab 2001
you know, i'll never understand those guys. i don't know how they do it.
i can't even talk to a woman i don't know...
...let alone yell out sexual suggestions at her from across the street.
well, you see, the men who make cat-calls are less inhibited than you or i.
they flout society's conventions in much the same way as the early modernist painters.
Why, these are the new artists of our generation— each cat-call a scathing critique on social role-play, every utterance of "bitch" or "sweet-tits" a comment on the human condition.
hmmm, i never thought of it like that. i suppose what i've seen, in my own myopic worldview, as vile and offensive is, in reality, a reflection of genius.
precisely. in many ways, we're witnessing the birth of a new Renaissance.
i want to eat hot lunch off your ass, you tasty little whore!
another masterpiece!

Rehabilitating Mr. Wiggles

you know, i just realized that i've been coasting through my whole existence.
instead of going out and seizing the day, i stayed in and slept through it.
instead of getting high off life, i got drunk off moonshine and the power i have over small animals.
©neil swaab 2001
instead of getting my foot in the door and starting a career, i stuck my penis in a water-melon and frightened the neighborhood children.
it's time to make some changes.
from this point on, you're going to see a whole new Mr. Wiggles.
let me guess, you're going to start fucking a different kind of produce now, right?
it helps if you warm it up first.
n. swaab

Mr. Wiggles, where do babies come from?
well Timmy, when a man and a woman love each other or get enough alcohol in their systems, they get into bed and play a naked game together.
afterwards, the man feels guilty because he couldn't play as long as the woman needed to and says that he'll call, but he never does.
she cries her eyes out for weeks until they run into each other on the street and she asks him why he never called when he said he would.
he lies and says that he wanted to but couldn't because his feelings were **too strong**.
©neil swaab 2001
the woman, insecure and looking for affection, believes him and gladly accepts him back into her bed for more naked games until, several weeks later, she notices that a friend who used to visit her once a month has stopped coming.
she then pees into this plastic thing and sees a "+" sign and says, "fuck! how could this happen!? i was on the pill!" and tells the man that she's pregnant.
he says, "how do i know it's even mine?" and she gets upset and says that she never has one night stands, but he says, "yeah, right. you did it with **me**, you probably do it with **every-body**, you slut," and she slaps him.
then he says, "fuck this shit!" and leaves. event-ually, when he's cooled off, he returns out of some sort of obligation to do "what's right".
he gets an extra job and she gets so fat that he doesn't want to play naked games with her anymore until, after nine months, this mucous-covered, shit-producing, money-draining child gets born into the world and the "family" lives happily ever after.
gee, Mr. Wiggles, making babies sure sounds **complicated**.
nah, not really, Timmy. all you gotta do is stick your penis in some girl's vagina.
n.swaab

dateless again on another Friday night, huh?
please, mr. wiggles. i've decided to focus on my career rather than girls.
©neil swaab 2001
Ha! Ha! Ha! Ha! Ha! Ha! Ha!
oh man, i needed that!
i'm so lonely.
n. swaab

come on! cook, damn you! cook!
you know, Mr. Wiggles, a watched pot doesn't boil.
©neil swaab 2002
really? i'll have to remember that.
bubble... bubble...
tsss!
ahhh!!! my face! my beautiful face!
n. swaab

Rehabilitating Mr. Wiggles

i used to be just like you.
©neil swaab 2002
i'd go to wild sex parties and orgies and do all sorts of heinous acts purely in the name of satisfying my tingly organs.
i was a sex goddess, capable of untold carnal pleasures.
but then i found Jesus. he cured me of my addiction and made me realize that i had more to offer the world than a three-input bliss factory.
now i hand out bibles in front of the school all day and spend nights knitting home made quilts for the lord. **praise Jesus!**
what a waste.
n.swaab
don't look at me. i swear i never seen that bitch before in my life.
©neil swaab 2002
ha! ha! ha!
crack!
n.swaab

ACKNOWLEDGEMENTS

I would like to thank all the editors and art directors I've dealt with in regards to this comic for taking a risk and giving me a chance to express myself. This list is comprised of Stacey Martin and Dan Dippel at *The Daily Orange Newspaper*, BJ Hammerstein at *Real Detroit Weekly*, Russ Smith, John Strausbaugh, Lisa Kearns, and Roxy Wu at *The NY Press*, and Bob Guccione Jr., Michael Martin, and Jennifer Morton at *Gear Magazine*. I would also like to thank my friends and family for supporting me and, while not necessarily understanding the work I do, at least not holding it against me. In particular I'd like to thank my parents, Bruce and Barbara Swaab, my grandparents, Irv and Bea Vinakour and Joan Ellis, my brother Adam Swaab (who co-authored the last Future-Me comic), Maria Gililova, Jen Szeto, and Scott Brant.